Table Of Contents

OBJECTIVE

- The objective of this course is to provide the operator the theoretical knowledge that is required by O.S.H.A. standards in order to drive a high risk vehicle.

- This course will consist of the following topics:

  - Overview of O.S.H.A. Requirements
  - Heavy Lift Basics
  - Safety Inspection
  - Daily Checklist
  - Heavy Lift Operation
  - Safety while Operating
  - Load Handling

- Following the end of this course, there will be an exam to test the operator's theoretical knowledge. The operator must pass with a score of 75% or above.

- After the course exam, the operator(s) will begin the practical phase of the course.

2.

INTRODUCTION & DEFINITION

CHAPTER 1

Session Objectives

☑ Understand how forklifts work.

☑ Operate a forklift safely and skillfully.

☑ Identify operating hazards.

☑ Apply general principles of safe operation.

☑ Properly inspect and maintain a forklift.

DEFINITION

OPERATORS MUST RECEIVE:

    ☑ **CLASSROOM TRAINING COVERING SAFETY RULES.**

    ☑ **BASIC MATERIAL-HANDLING TECHNIQUES.**

    ☑ **BASIC OPERATING TECHNIQUES.**

    ☑ **DRIVER'S PERFORMANCE TEST.**

DEFINITION

CCR Title 8 Section 3668

CCR- SAFETY AND HEALTH STANDARDS

Title 8 - GENERAL INDUSTRY

Section 3668 - POWERED INDUSTRIAL TRUCKS

HOW MOST INJURIES OCCUR

☑ **OVERLOADING CAUSING THE VEHICLE TO TURNOVER.**

☑ **LOAD INSTABILITY CAUSING TURNOVER.**

☑ **OBSTRUCTIONS IN THE PATH OF TRAVEL OR LIFT.**

☑ **USING FORKLIFT OUTSIDE OF DESIGN LIMITATIONS.**

☑ **STRIKING A PEDESTRIAN.**

DEFINITION

Effective Powered Industrial Truck Operator Training Program

Four major areas of concern must be addressed:

❑ The general hazards that apply to the operation of all or most powered industrial trucks;

❑ The hazards associated with the operation of particular types of trucks;

❑ The hazards of workplaces generally; and,

❑ The hazards of the particular workplace where the vehicle operates.

Certification

YOUR INSTRUCTOR Shall certify that each operator has been trained and evaluated as required by the standard.

Certification shall include:

❑ Name of operator.

❑ Date of training.

❑ Date of evaluation.

❑ Identity of person performing the training or evaluation.

Classes of Commonly-Used Powered Industrial Trucks*

The Industrial Truck Association has placed powered industrial trucks into 7 classes.

   Class I - Electric motor rider trucks.

   Class II - Electric motor narrow aisle trucks.

   Class III - Electric motor hand trucks or hand/rider trucks.

   Class IV - Internal combustion engine trucks (solid/cushion tires).

   Class V - Internal combustion engine trucks (pneumatic tires).

   Class VI - Electric and internal combustion engine tractors.

   Class VII - Rough terrain forklift trucks.

   Note that this classification refers to commonly-used vehicles and does not
include all powered industrial trucks covered by the O.S.H.A. standard.

Operator Qualifications

It is the Employer's responsibility to ensure that:

- The operator is competent and capable of performing all job tasks.

- The operator receives formal theoretical and practical training.

- The operator evaluated by their Supervisor and HSE.

CHAPTER 2

CAL/O.S.H.A. Standards

**Subchapter 7. General Industry Safety Orders
Group 4. General Mobile Equipment and
Auxiliaries
Article 25. Industrial Trucks, Tractors, Haulage
Vehicles, and Earthmoving Equipment**

§3668. Powered Industrial Truck Operator Training

(a) Safe Operation.

(1) The employer shall ensure that each powered industrial truck operator is competent to operate a powered industrial truck safely, as demonstrated by the successful completion of the training and evaluation specified in this section.

(2) Prior to permitting an employee to operate a powered industrial truck (except for training purposes), the employer shall ensure that each operator has successfully completed the training required by this section, except as permitted in subsection (e).

(b) Training program implementation. Trainees may operate a powered industrial truck only:

(1) Under the direct supervision of persons who have the knowledge, training and experience to train operators and evaluate their competence; and

(2) Where such operation does not endanger the trainee or other employees.

(3) Training shall consist of a combination of formal instruction (e.g., lecture, discussion, interactive computer learning, video tape, written material), practical training (demonstrations performed by the trainer and practical exercises performed by the trainee) and evaluation of the operator's performance in the workplace.

(4) All operator training and evaluation shall be conducted by persons who have the knowledge, training and experience to train powered industrial truck operators and evaluate their competence.

§3668. Powered Industrial Truck Operator Training

(c) Training program content. Powered industrial truck operators shall receive initial training in the following topics, except in topics which the employer can demonstrate are not applicable to the safe operation of the truck in the employer's workplace.

(1) Truck-related topics:
(A) Operating instructions, warnings, and precautions for the types of truck the operator will be authorized to operate;
(B) Differences between the truck and the automobile;
(C) Truck controls and instrumentation: where they are located, what they do, and how they work;
(D) Engine or motor operation;
(E) Steering and maneuvering;
(F) Visibility (including restrictions due to loading);
(G) Fork and attachment adaptation, operation, and use limitations;
(H) Vehicle capacity;
(I) Vehicle stability;
(J) Any vehicle inspection and maintenance that the operator will be required to perform;
(K) Refueling and/or charging and recharging of batteries;
(L) Operating limitations;
(M) Any other operating instructions, warnings, or precautions listed in the operator's manual for the types of vehicle that the employee is being trained to operate.
(2) Workplace-related topics:
(A) Surface conditions where the vehicle will be operated;
(B) Composition of loads to be carried and load stability;
(C) Load manipulation, stacking, and unstacking;
(D) Pedestrian traffic in areas where the vehicle will be operated;
(E) Narrow aisles and other restricted places where the vehicle will be operated;
(F) Hazardous (classified) locations where the vehicle will be operated;
(G) Ramps and other sloped surfaces that could affect the vehicle's stability;
(H) Closed environments and other areas where insufficient ventilation or poor vehicle maintenance could cause a build-up of carbon monoxide or diesel exhaust;
(I) Other unique or potentially hazardous conditions in the workplace that could affect safe operation.

(d) Refresher training and evaluation. Refresher training, including an evaluation of the effectiveness of that training, shall be conducted as required by subsection (d)(1) to ensure that the operator has the knowledge and skills needed to operate the powered industrial truck safely.

(1) Refresher training in relevant topics shall be provided to the operator when:

(A) The operator has been observed to operate the vehicle in an unsafe manner;

(B) The operator has been involved in an accident or near-miss incident;

(C) The operator has received an evaluation that reveals that the operator is not operating the truck safely;

(D) The operator is assigned to drive a different type of truck; or

(E) A condition in the workplace changes in a manner that could affect safe operation of the truck.

(2) An evaluation of each powered industrial truck operator's performance shall be conducted at least once every three years.

(e) Avoidance of duplicative training. If an operator has previously received training in a topic specified in subsection (c) of this section, and such training is appropriate to the truck and working conditions encountered, additional training in that topic is not required if the operator has been evaluated and found competent to operate the truck safely.

(f) Certification. The employer shall certify that each operator has been trained and evaluated as required by this section. The certification shall include the name of the operator, the date of the training, the date of the evaluation, and the identity of the person(s) performing the training or evaluation.

(g) Dates. The employer shall ensure that operators of powered industrial trucks are trained, as appropriate, in accordance with the following dates:

(1) If the employee was hired before July 15, 2000, the initial training and evaluation of that employee must be completed by July 15, 2000;

(2) If the employee was hired after July 15, 2000, the initial training and evaluation of that employee must be completed before the employee is assigned to operate a powered industrial truck.

Exception: Agricultural operations as defined in Section 3437 of the General Industry Safety Orders are exempt from the requirements of Section 3668.

Note: Authority cited: Section 142.3, Labor Code. Reference: Section 142.3, Labor Code.

Principals of Operation

CHAPTER 3

Forklift vs. Automobile

- **Rear of a forklift swings in opposite direction of the turn.**

- **Forklift impact against objects magnified.**

- **Drives backward and forward.**

- **One hand on controls.**

Safety Rules of the Road

➢ **Avoid running over loose objects.**

➢ **Yield to pedestrians**
   - **Observe all traffic regulations.**
   - **Max speed limit is (12 mph) without a load.**
   - **Max speed limit is (6 mph) with a load.**

➢ **Under normal traffic conditions keep to the right.**

➢ **Keep a clear view of the path of travel.**

Picking up a Load

- **Keep your mast vertical.**
- **Load should touch carriage.**
- **Lift to clear the floor (approximately 4 inches).**
- **Check for clearance.**
- **Look for overhead obstructions.**
- **Watch for pedestrians.**
- **Proceed to your destination.**

Determine a Load's Center of Gravity

- **Center of gravity is the balance point.**

- **Load center is the point where the heaviest part of the load is located.**

- **Pick up load on the side closest to its center of gravity.**

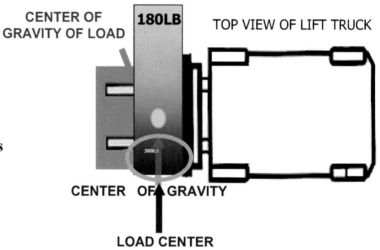

Stability Triangle

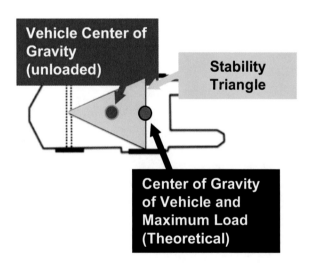

Vehicle Center of Gravity (unloaded)

Stability Triangle

Center of Gravity of Vehicle and Maximum Load (Theoretical)

What Can Cause a Tip over?

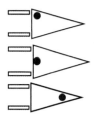

- Center of gravity side to side.
- Center of gravity forward.
- Center of gravity backward.

Combination of actions or circumstances can cause tip over.

Drive Types

- Some Heavy lifts use all four tires to turn, bending in at the center to allow the machine to move.
- Some Heavy Lifts have front wheel drive.

DEPENDING ON THE LIFT THE

CENTER OF GRAVITY CAN AND WILL

CHANGE

Drive Types

- Is the area free from debris?
- Line the Heavy Lift up squarely.
- Stop the Heavy Lift's movement.
- Tilt the mast forward so that it is straight up & down.
- If necessary "sides shift" to center the load.
- Lower the mast down to the point that the weight of the load is fully in contact with the surface you are placing it on.
- Avoid slack in the chains.
- Slowly back away from the load.

In Case of Fire

- Fires do start from time to time due to poor housekeeping and faulty electrical equipment or overheating of the engine compartment.

- In case of a fire follow these following steps:
  - If safe, eliminate the fuel source by closing the fuel value (If so equipped).
  - Shut off the ignition and get out of the machine.
  - Grease fires, when caught soon enough rarely produce enough heat to ignite the diesel fuel, so you're usually dealing with a small fire
  - If the fire extinguisher on the lift is designed to cut off the source of oxygen, without oxygen the fire should go out. The best way to avoid a fire is to keep the engine area clear of debris and leaks and grease.
  - When putting out a grease or gas fire, aim the extinguisher at the base of the flame.

REMEMBER: IF A FIRE LOOKS TOO BIG FOR ONE EXTINGUISHER TO HANDLE, DO NOT TRY.

LEAVE THE AREA.

Accidents involving pedestrians may be caused by:

- **Obstructed view**

- **Turning**

- **Speeding**

Pedestrian unaware;

O.S.H.A. STATES PEDESTRIAN HAS THE RIGHT OF WAY.

Any Company has the right to implement a SAFER PROGRAM

which OVERRIDES O.S.H.A. in any case.

Operating Hazards- Environmental Conditions

- **Combustible fuel-operated forklift in poorly ventilated area.**

- **Traveling on ramps.**

- **Slippery floors.**

- **Operating on dirt or gravel.**

- **Poor lighting.**

- **Crossing railroad tracks.**

Operating Hazards - Load Carrying

- **Working around loading docks.**

- **Loads that block the forward vision.**

- **Stacking and unstacking on racks.**

What's wrong Here?

Forks not fully lowered.

Forklift parked on sloped surface.

Operating a Forklift

- **Authorized operators only.**

- **Quickly report accidents.**

- **Always wear seat belts.**

- **No person under the forks.**

- **Operate controls only from driver's seat.**

- **Always use a SPOTTER when possible.**

Tip over Safety Procedure

- **Always wear your seat belt.**

- **Hold onto the steering wheel.**

- **Press your chest tight against the steering wheel.**

- **Brace your feet.**

- **Lean away from the fall.**

Loading and Unloading

- **Never overload forklift.**

- **Check load weight.**

- **Locate load's center of gravity.**

- **Inspect the load.**

- **Restack or secure unstable loads.**

- **Be sure forks are under load.**

- **Tow from rear towing pin.**

Traveling

- **Look in the direction of travel.**

- **Keep body inside cage.**

- **Keep forks low when traveling.**

- **Sound the horn.**

- **Don't speed.**

- **Check clearance.**

Traveling Continued

- **Avoid loose objects or Pot-Holes**

- **Never carry passengers**

- **Pedestrians have the right-of-way**

- **Keep a safe distance**

- **From the edge of ramps or docks**

- **NO CELL PHONES while operating machines**

- **No horseplay**

High Stacking

- **Never approach at an angle.**

- **Center the truck in the area you are high stacking.**

- **Stop the truck & adjust mast so it is straight up and down.**

- **Also center any attachments.**

- **Raise the mast up to the area of the load.**

- **You may need a spotter.**

Ramps and Railroads

- **No turns on a ramp.**

- **Load facing upgrade.**

- **Go slow.**

- **Cross railroad tracks diagonally.**

- **Never park within 8 feet of the center of railroad tracks.**

Travel Distance

- Maintain a safe distance of **3 truck lengths.**

- Keep your truck under control at all times.

- Never pass a forklift going in the same direction.

- Slow down & sound your horn at intersections, blind spots or dangerous locations.

Keep a Distance of 3 Truck Lengths

Docks

- **Inspect the dock plate**

- **Check the trailer floor condition**

- **Make sure trailer wheels are chocked**

- **Ensure that the nose of the trailer is supported**

Parking

- **Don't block exits or aisles.**

- **Lower the forks.**

- **Set gear to neutral.**

- **Set the parking brake.**

- **Turn off the key.**

- **Chock the Tires when on incline.**

Forklift Inspection

CHAPTER 4

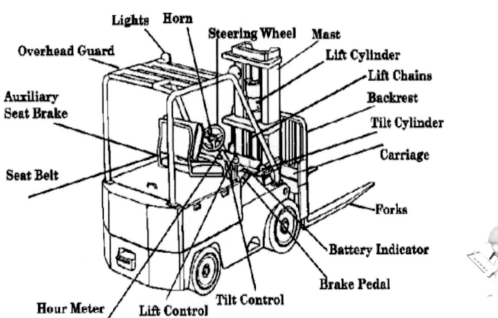

Components of a Forklift

Forklift Inspections

Daily Checkout Sheet

Two part checkout procedure.

➤ *Walk around & Operational check*

- Reduce downtime
- Increase productivity
- Risk reduction

FORKLIFT OPERATOR'S DAILY CHECKLIST

(Complete Before The Start of Each Shift)

DATE	TRUCK NO	BUILDING NO	SHIFT
☐ INTERNAL COMBUSTION	☐ ELECTRIC	HOUR METER START END TOTAL HRS	
OPERATOR'S SIGNATURE		SUPERVISOR'S SIGNATURE	

CHECK ANY DEFECTIVE ITEM WITH AN X AND GIVE DETAILS BELOW

ACCELERATOR	HOUR METER
ALARMS	HYDRAULIC CONTROLS
BATTERY CONNECTOR	LIGHTS - HEAD AND TAIL
BATTERY - DISCHARGE INDICATOR	LIGHTS - WARNING
BELTS	MAST
BRAKES - PARKING	OIL LEAKS
BRAKES - SERVICE	OIL PRESSURE
CABLES	OVERHEAD GUARD
ENGINE OIL LEVEL	RADIATOR LEVEL
FORKS	SAFETY EQUIPMENT
FUEL LEVEL	STEERING
GAUGES	TIRES
HORN	UNUSUAL NOISES
HOSES	OTHER

DETAILS: _____

_____

_____

_____

_____

_____

MAINTENANCE COPY

Forklift Inspections; Continued

Part 1 - The Walk Around

❑ **Operators name**

❑ **The date**

❑ **Serial number or unit number of the vehicle**

❑ **Hour meter reading**

❑ **What shift are you using the forklift on**

❑ **What day of the week it is**

❑ **Forks**

❑ **Warning Decals**

❑ **Operators Manual**

❑ **Load Back Rest**

❑ **Hydraulic Oil**

❑ **Radiator Fluid**

❑ **Tires & Wheels**

❑ **Engine Oil**

❑ **Sheet Metal Covers**

❑ **Battery Connectors**

❑ **Overhead Guard**

Forklift Inspections

Part 2 – PRE - OPERATION

❑   Service Brake – Functioning Smoothly

❑ Accelerator or Direction Control Pedal – Functioning Smoothly

❑ Parking Brake – Functioning Smoothly

❑ Drive Control – Forward/Reverse – Functioning Smoothly

❑ Tilt Control – Forward and Back – Functioning Smoothly

❑ Hoist and Lowering Control – Functioning Smoothly

❑ Attachment Control – Operation

❑ Horn and Lights – Functioning

❑ Cab (if equipped) – Heater, Defroster, Wipers – Functioning

❑ Gauges: Ammeter, Oil Pressure, Hour Meter, Fuel, Temp.,

Nameplate

- OSHA requires a legible nameplate

- It includes information about the forklift and attachments

- It lists the maximum load capacity

- It describes the load center

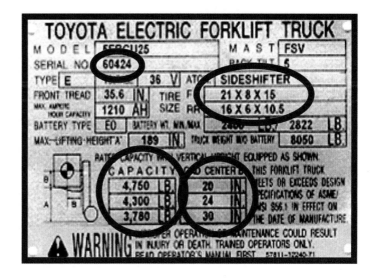

The Walk Around Inspection

Before operation, a Daily Safety & Maintenance Checklist is required to be completed.

It is important to perform a proper inspection before use of the equipment to avoid safety hazards and equipment failure. The checklist involves a Walk Around of the equipment and contains specific areas to focus on.

The walk around generally requires the following to be checked:

- Forks
- Warning Decals
- Load Back Rest
- Tires and Wheels
- Sheet metal Doors/Covers
- Battery Terminals

- Outside of the ROPS/Windows/Doors
- Pins
- Handholds/Ladders
- Underneath
- Cleanliness Outside

Carriage and Load Backrest

- Are carriage bars straight, not bent?

- The notches on the top of the carriage bar are they worn down to the point the fork lock will not lock in place?

- Does the carriage roll up and down smoothly in the mast channels?

- The chains mounted to the carriage are they the correct tension?

- Are the chains lubricated, they should not be rusty or dry.

- The Load Backrest should be straight and not twisted or cracked. All fasteners need to be secure.

Transmission & Transfer Case

- Look at the transmission area for leaks or damage.
- Do not operate if a visible leak is found.

Steps & Handholds

- Inspect the ladder and the handholds on the machine.

- Do not operate machine if any of the rungs of the ladder are missing on the left (drivers) side of the machine.

- Do not operate the machine if lose or missing handholds are present on the machine.

Fuel Tank

- Inspect the tank for damage.
- Do not operate the lift if fuel is leaking from the tank.
- Ensure that the areas around the tank are clean

Axles

- Inspect the front and rear differential for leaks or damage.
- Do not operate the machine if a visible leak is found.
- Check the inside of the wheels for brake fluid leaks.
- Usually fluid will splatter on the tire if a leak is present.
- Do not operate if a visible leak is found.

Hydraulic Tank

- Ensure the fluid level is in the safe range. The hydraulic tank may be checked either when engine is hot or cold

- Do not operate the lift is any leaks from the hydraulic tank are found on the ground.

- The hydraulic tank must be checked with the clamps closed and forks on the ground.

NEVER open the hydraulic tank while the vehicle is running!

Transmission Oil

- Ensure the fluid levels on the dipstick or sight glass are in the proper operating range.
- Report low levels to your supervisor before operating the machine.

Front and Rear Lights

- With the help of another operator, confirm all the lights are working. The lift may only be operated during daylight hours if lights are missing or not working.

- Do not operate the lift in the day or night if the safety beacon light is not functioning.

Battery Compartment

- Do not operate the machine if a battery is not secured or the cover is missing.
- Ensure that all terminals are clean

Engine Oil

- Ensure fluid level is in the safe operating range listed on the dipstick.

- If fluid level is low or none is found on the dipstick, then do not operate the machine. Contact your supervisor.

Engine Coolant

- Look at the sight glass to ensure fluid is present in the window.

- Only for **Forklifts without a sight glass,** remove the radiator cap from the forklift if you **know** the lift is cold.

- Never open a hot radiator cap.

- Ensure the fluid in radiator is topped off or fluid is present in the sight glass.

Radiator

- Inspect the radiator for leaks.

- Ensure the fins of the radiator are not blocked and air is flowing from all areas.

- Do not operate the machine if fluid is leaking from the radiator.

Fuel Filters/Water Separator

All Belts

- Check belts for tension, wear, or cracks.

- Contact the maintenance department and supervisor if problems with the belt are discovered.

Air Filter

- The air filter should be cleaned from the inside out
- Frequency of cleaning is located in the operators manual
- A facemask is required to clean the filter

Overall Engine Compartment

- Keep engine area free of oil, buildup, and trash to detect and prevent leaks and other problems.

- If an area is leaking, report to maintenance department and your supervisor.

ROPS

- Check the Roll Over Protection System (**ROPS**) for cracks, damage or missing bolts.

- Contact supervisor before operating the machine if damage or missing bolts are discovered.

FIRE EXTINGUISHER

- Ensure the fire extinguisher is charged, and undamaged.

- Do not operate the machine with a faulty fire extinguisher.

Windshield & Window

- Inspect the windshield for cracks to ensure glass will not break while operating the machine.

- Report all questionable cracks or damage to your supervisor before operating the machine.

- If a lift develops a crack during the shift, report the damage to your supervisor.

Windshield Wipers

- Inspect the wipers for wear or damage.
- If rain is present, do not operate the machine with damaged or missing wipers.

Seat

- Adjust the seat to proper adjustment based on height and weight of the operator.

- If seat will not adjust to the proper height, not allowing the operator to reach the pedals of the machine, contact the maintenance department before operating the machine.

Seatbelt & Mounting

- Inspect the seatbelt for wear or damage.

- Seatbelt should extend and retract with no hang-ups

- Insure the seatbelt fits snugly and does not have any knots

- Do not operate the machine if seatbelt is missing or damaged.

  8 out of 10 accident cases, a worker will get ejected from their cab and pinned by their own machine because the operator didn't
  WEAR THEIR SEATBELT!!!

Horn, Backup Alarm, Backup Camera

- Ensure the horn, backup alarm, and backup camera is functional.
- Do not operate the machine if these components are not functional.

Mirrors

- Ensure the mirrors are adjusted for optimum visibility.
- Do not operate the machine if the mirrors are missing.

Cab Air Filter

- Blow the filter out daily with compressed air before operating the machine.

Gauges, Indicators, Switches, Controls

- Note problems with these components on checklist and report to the maintenance department.

- Check for any engine lights or warnings that will appear in the outlined areas.

Service and Parking Brake Check

- Perform the service and park brake daily for each machine operated.

- Do not operate the machine if the lift fails the park or service brake test.

- When testing the parking and emergency brakes keep in mind that the lower range gears (1&2) are powerful enough to drive through the brakes and burn them out.

Inching/Flash Pedal

- Ensure the inching pedal stops travel with smooth deceleration.

- Do not operate if the inching pedal fails to stop travel.

- When using the "inching" or "flash" pedal, be sure to check the settings and know how this system works on your machine. It could be dangerous for you or your surroundings if you neglect checking or knowing about this feature.

Safety First!

- **O.S.H.A**. requires that an operator will be expected to have the knowledge to inspect their vehicle.

- If any items are found to be damaged or defective you must contact your supervisor immediately.

All Forklifts

- ❏ *STOP FORKLIFT*

- ❏ *LOWER FORKS to the Ground*

- ❏ *SET PARKING BREAK*

- ❏ *TURN OFF IGNITION*

- ❏ *CHOCK TIRE when on an incline*

CHOCKS

WRONG   RIGHT

Safety and Heavy Lifts
(Location Specific)

During this section, it is the instructor's responsibility to identify all areas in the yard of their specific location that contain:

- **Rough terrain**

- **Overhead hazards (POWERLINES) ???**

- **Pedestrian traffic**

- **Other hazardous areas that must be known**

Safety & Maintenance
Inspection

A thorough pre-inspection consists of both visual and operational checks. During the inspection you'll be looking for three main types of failures that could create a danger to you, your team, or company property. Loose, missing or broken parts, fluid leaks and malfunctioning systems.

The two part checkout procedure known as the Walk Around & Operational

Check List :

- **<u>Reduces downtime</u>**
- **<u>Increases productivity</u>**
- **<u>Reduces risk</u>**
- **<u>Is required under O.S.H.A. and HESA</u>**
- **<u>Prevents accidents that result from mechanical failure</u>**

Safety & Heavy Lifts

Safety is of the utmost importance when operating heavy vehicles. Each heavy vehicle must have the following before operation or is otherwise tagged out immediately:

- A service brake system, emergency brake system and a parking brake system

- Working headlights, tail lights and brake lights

- An audible horn and backup alarm

- Intact windshield with working windshield wipers

- Rollover protection system

- Fire Extinguisher

- Seat belt

Heavy Lift Basics

- A Heavy Lift is a type of Front-end Loader. These loaders have multiple types of attachments that can be used for different purposes in many industrial working zones.

- Heavy Lifts are primarily used for the transportation of pipe, accessories and coils

- **There are two main types of Front-end Loaders**

  - ➤ **Rigid-frame**
    - Rigid Frame loaders have a one piece frame to which various attachments can connected to. The most common attachment seen in a pipe yard is the fork attachment with clamps.
  - ➤ **Articulated frame**
    - The articulated frame loaders have a two piece body which allows it to pivot at one point, usually in the middle of the lift.
    - The cab can sit either in front of or behind the pivot point

Condition of Forks

- Check forks for visible cracking, if they are bent, or if the ends of the forks are curled too far up or down.

- The lift should not be operated if the forks are bent, or if visible cracks are shown.

All Hoses

- Inspect all hoses for cracks and wear.
- Do not operate the machine if fluid is leaking from the hoses.

Loader Frame & Arms

- Check for straightness, cracks or any damage.

- Report damage to components to supervisor before operating the machine.

Pins

- The lift shall not be operated if any of the pins are broken or missing.

- Grease for pins should be added only through the Zerk fittings. Grease on the outside doesn't help lubricate the pin and only attracts dirt

- Frequency of grease application is in the operators manual and is also posted on the inside of the engine compartment door

Air Tank

- Drain the moisture in the air tank daily.
- Make sure you don't see or hear any leaks from the tank.

(As a general rule, PSI is up to manufacture recommendations)

Underneath Machine

- Look under the machine for fluid leaks or visible damage to the components.

- Do not operate the lift if fresh fluid is found on the ground.

- If fluid leaks on the machine but not on the ground clean with a pressure washer and monitor in wash bay only.

Grapple Attachment

- A grapple attachment simply works like a pair of tongs. You open it up on approach, slide the forks underneath the load, and then you clamp it down. You hang onto the load by keeping the clamps closed.

  - Check for any cracks, bends or twists in the structure.
  - Check for leaks from hoses and cylinders.
  - Does the attachment operate smoothly with no binding

Hydraulic Lines

- Check all the hydraulic lines and fittings inside and out of the machine for leaks, cracks, or frays.

- Do not operate the machine when fluid is leaking on the ground from fittings or lines.

Tires, Wheels, Stem
Caps & Lug Nuts

- Check tires for excessive wear, cracks, or damage.

- Check the rim and split ring for damage.

- Ensure the lug nuts and stem are present on the wheel.

- Check the air pressure on the tire for correct PSI.

Remember:

DO NOT operate the lift if a tire has a deep sidewall crack with wire or air leaking from the damaged area. All missing or damaged areas to rim, tire, or hub shall be reported to supervisor before operating the machine.

Attachments

- **Change operating clearances**

- **Change capacity**

- **Change stability and load center**

Heavy Lift Basics

- Carry Lift   (Pettibone)

Heavy Lift Basics

- Heavy Forklift (Hyster)

Heavy Lift Basics

- Front Loader (John Deere)

High Reach Forklift
INSPECTIONS

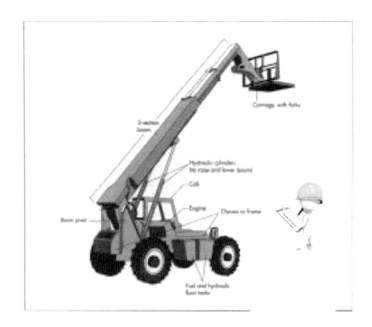

High Reach Forklift
INSPECTIONS

High Reach Forklift
INSPECTIONS

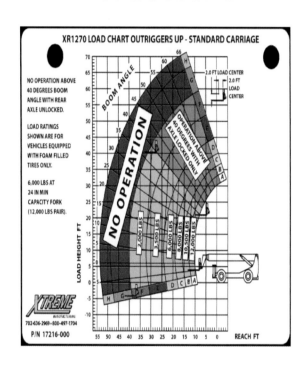

High Reach Forklift
INSPECTIONS

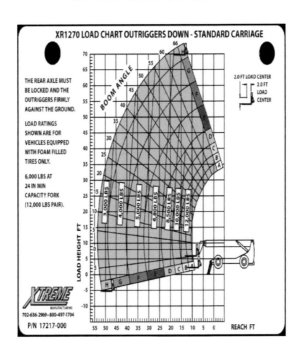

Forklift INSPECTIONS

OSHA Studies

OSHA studies have clearly shown that unsafe and or improper operation are the major cause of most accidents resulting in fatalities, or serious injuries.
A well defined operator training program is the key too to accident reduction in the workplace.

Power Line Safety

CHAPTER 5

OSHA 29 CFR 1926.1408   also requires that you do the following:

➢Conduct a planning meeting {tailgate}

➢If tag lines are used, they must be non-conductive

➢Erect and maintain an elevated warning line(s) at 20' from the power line
for unknown voltage.

Power Line Safety

➤Requires that you choose from one of the following three options when working near power lines that are up to 350kV.

(1) De-energized and grounded
(2) 20' clearance
(3) Use the clearances listed in Table A

Required clearance for operations near high voltage power lines:	
to 50 kV	10 ft. (3.05m)
over 50 to 200 kV	15 ft. (4.60m)
over 200 to 350 kV	20 ft. (6.10m)
over 350 to 500 kV	25 ft. (7.62m)
over 500 to 750 kV	35 ft. (10.67m)
over 750 to 1000 kV	45 ft. (13.72m)

kV = kilovolt (1000 volts) a unit of electrical potential difference.

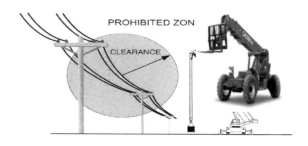

OSHA & ASME BOTH REQUIRE A MINIMUM OF 20' CLEARANCE FOR UNKNOWN VOLTAGE

Power Line Safety

CLEARANCES WHILE IN TRANSIT
NO LOAD

OSHA 29 CFR 1926.1411
ASME B30.5

UP TO 0.75kV.. 4'
0.75kV to 50kV...….. 6'
50kV to 345kV... 10'
345kV to 740kV.. 16'
750kV to 1,000kV... 20'

CHAPTER 4
POWERLINE SAFETY

Power Line Safety

IF THE FORKLIFT COME INTO CONTACT WITH THE POWER LINES

➢ **DON'T PANIC! YOU SHOULD BE SAFE AS LONG AS YOU STAY AT A CONSTANT VOLTAGE WITHIN THE CAB**

➢ IF YOU ARE ON THE VEHICLE AND YOUR LIFE IS IN DANGER   {I.E. FIRE}

➢ EXIT THE VEHICLE WITHOUT MAKING SIMULTANEOUS
➢ CONTACT WITH THE GROUND AND THE VEHICLE

➢ **(DO NOT walk or run)**

➢ BUNNY HOP AWAY WITH BOTH FEET TOGETHER
   OR SHUFFLE YOUR FEET

Power Line Safety

DON'T LET THIS HAPPEN TO YOU !!!!!!!!!!

Spotter Duties

CHAPTER 6

THE SPOTTER'S RESPONSIBILITIES

▶ Always be sure to use the same signals for the same moves (avoid misunderstandings)

▶ Hand signals are much better than vocal signals. Because of noise, a shouted signal may not be heard or may be misunderstood.

▶ If the driver is unclear at any point about the spotter's signals, the vehicle should be stopped immediately. Never assume what the spotter is signaling, if there is any doubt

Spotter Duties

Industries Where Powered Industrial Truck Accidents Occurred

Industry	# Accidents Investigated by OSHA
Mining	4
Construction	25
Manufacturing	95
Transportation, Communication, Utilities	22
Wholesale Trades	25
Retail Trades	18
Service	7
Public Administration	4
Total	200

Spotter Duties

Industries Where Powered Industrial Truck Accidents Occurred

BEING STRUCK BY, OR CAUGHT IN- BETWEEN, ARE TWO OF THE LEADING CAUSE OF INJURIES AND FATALITIES ON CONSTRUCTION SITES!

STRUCK BY (22%)

CAUGHT IN-BETWEEN (18%)

Spotter Duties

Vehicle / Heavy Equipment   Danger Zone

▸ Blind spots
▸ Rotating machinery
▸ Swing radius
▸ Travel Path
▸ Approaching the machinery before acknowledging the operator
▸ Non-essential workers on the area
▸ Struck by overhead loads falling

IF YOU CAN TOUCH THE MACHINERY
YOU ARE TOO CLOSE!!!

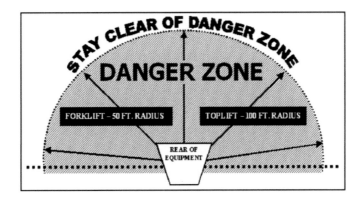

Spotter Duties

Learn to know the…

Danger-ZONE

THE SHADED AREA SURROUNDING
EACH VEHICLE REPRESENTS THE
DANGER ZONE IN WHICH THE
VEHICLE OPERATOR'S VIEW OF
PEDESTRAN TRAFFIC IS GREATLY
REDUCED OR OBSCURRED
ALTOGETHER.

Spotter Duties

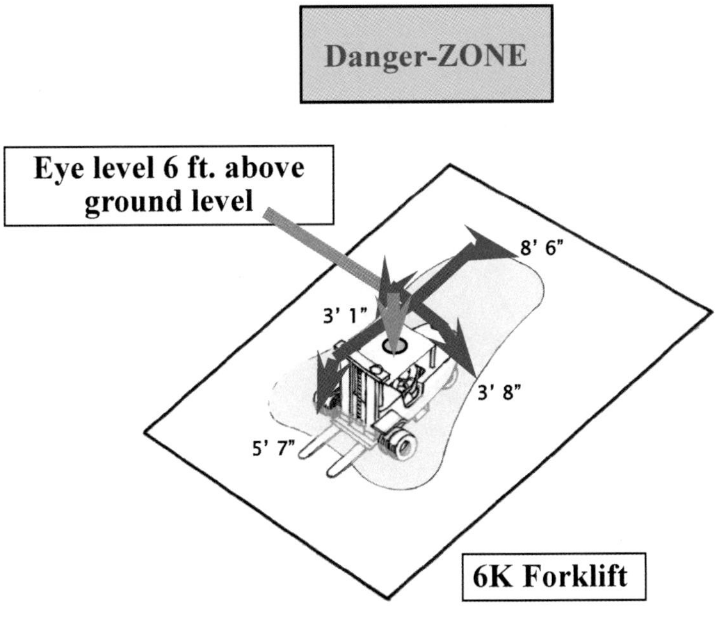

Danger-ZONE

Eye level 6 ft. above ground level

8' 6"

3' 1"

3' 8"

5' 7"

6K Forklift

Spotter Duties

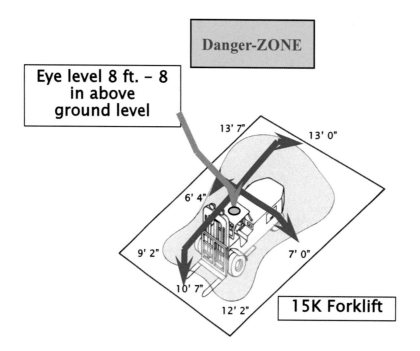

Danger-ZONE

Eye level 8 ft. – 8 in above ground level

13' 7"   13' 0"

6' 4"

9' 2"   7' 0"

10' 7"

12' 2"   15K Forklift

Spotter Duties

Danger–ZONE

Eye level 8 ft. - 9 in above ground level

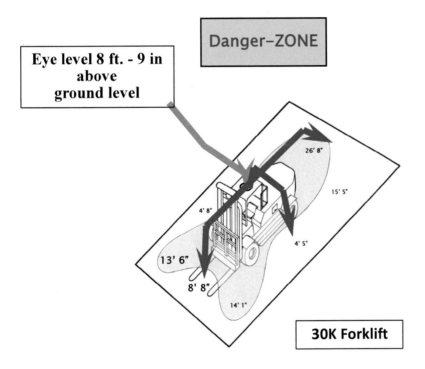

26' 8"

15' 5"

4' 8"

4' 5"

13' 6"

8' 8"

14' 1"

30K Forklift

Spotter Duties

Danger–ZONE

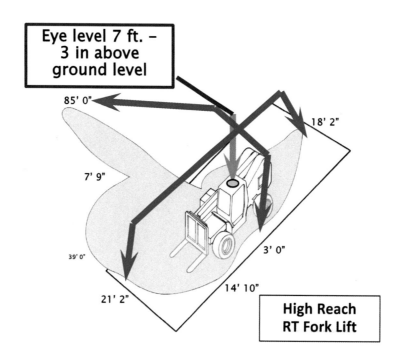

Eye level 7 ft. –
3 in above
ground level

85' 0"

18' 2"

7' 9"

3' 0"

39' 0"

14' 10"

21' 2"

High Reach
RT Fork Lift

Spotter Duties

Vehicle / Heavy Equipment Danger Zone

▶ Make sure no one enters the danger zone while the machinery is in operation, the danger zone is the area around the equipment/vehicle where the operator don't have a full visibility during normal operation. Stay at least ten feet away from all sides of the Machinery.

▶ Front.

▶ Both Sides (left, right) Yes, the right rear side is one of the most dangerous.

▶ Back Yes, behind the machinery is also one of the most dangerous.

▶ Up and Bottom.

Spotter Duties

Vehicle / Heavy Equipment Danger Zone

If you're working near moving vehicles or equipment, what are the most important safety points to remember?

1. Stay alert at all times.
2. Don't distract yourself.
3. Keep a safe distance.
4. Keep off the equipment unless authorized.
5. Watch out for shifting or unstable loads.
6. Wear a bright orange vest if you are working near moving vehicles or heavy equipment.
7. Wear reflectorize clothing at night.

Spotter Duties

SPOTTERS -AN IMPORTANT REQUIREMENT

There is the important rule for drivers and operators:

"Don't back up or move a heavy equipment unless you have a spotter directing your movement."

❖ **It's an easy rule to remember.**

❖ **The important thing is to obey it.**

Spotter Duties

When to use a Spotter

When:
- Backing a vehicle or machinery
- Entering or moving a vehicle or
- Machinery in a congested area
- Poor visibility
- Close proximity
- Pedestrians/coworkers or other contractors on the surroundings
- lateral, overhead, or other obstructions

Spotter Duties

SPOTTERS - AN IMPORTANT REQUIREMENT

This person has to watch out for others as well as for
himself / herself (keeping enough distance in between
spotter and equipment moving), and make sure the vehicle
doesn't damage property.
It may appear as an easy task but there are a lot of dangers
involved.

Spotter Duties

THE SPOTTER'S RESPONSIBILITIES

SPOTTERS AND DRIVERS/OPERATOR MUST WORK TOGETHER

The operator will discuss the positioning, backing, movement and plan with the spotter before proceeding.

The operator shall stop the vehicle immediately prior to losing sight or losing sight of the spotter.

Spotter Duties

THE SPOTTER'S RESPONSIBILITIES

In order to give you an unobstructed view of the entire movement, when directing the driver/operator, stand at the driver's side.
It's important that the driver understands your signals, so get together with the driver before any movement and explain the signals you will use.
Allow for sufficient stopping, distance and clearance

TO THE OPERATORS PERSPECTIVE

Spotter Duties

THE SPOTTER'S RESPONSIBILITIES

STRAIGHT BACKWARD OR FORWARD – To move the vehicle in a straight line either forward or backward.

Go Backwards

Go Forward

TO THE OPERATORS PERSPECTIVE

Spotter Duties

THE SPOTTER'S RESPONSIBILITIES

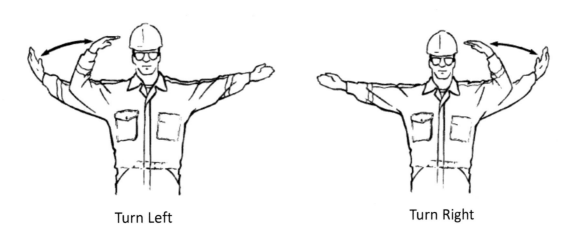

Turn Left   Turn Right

TO THE OPERATORS PERSPECTIVE

Spotter Duties

THE SPOTTER'S RESPONSIBILITIES

DISTANCE TO STOPPING POINT – To provide the driver a visual reference for the distance to the stop point.

TO THE OPERATORS PERSPECTIVE

Spotter Duties

THE SPOTTER'S RESPONSIBILITIES

CLEARED TO LEAVE THE AREA
– To show the driver the vehicle is clear of obstructions and is cleared to leave in the direction indicated.

TO THE OPERATORS PERSPECTIVE

Spotter Duties

THE SPOTTER'S RESPONSIBILITIES

STOP – Stop all movement
of the vehicle, await further
instructions.

**TO THE OPERATORS
PERSPECTIVE**

Spotter Duties

THE SPOTTER'S RESPONSIBILITIES

When spotting, concentrate on spotting –The
task at hand.
Maintain eye contact with the driver/operator,
even if you have to change position frequently.

If the spotter needs to stop spotting momentarily
for any reason, first make sure that the
driver/operator _stops_ the equipment.

Spotter Duties

BE SURE YOU'RE SEEN

If you or someone else have to pass behind a vehicle or equipment:

1. Stop the vehicle or equipment first.

2. As you're passing behind it, extend your hand at arm's length and place it against the back of the vehicle/equipment. Then if the vehicle/equipment starts to move, you'll be able to feel the movement and get out of the way.

Spotter Duties

BE SURE YOU'RE SEEN

In addition to standing well to the driver's side of the vehicle/equipment, wear a fluorescent vest.

In the dark, don't blind the driver by shining your flashlight in the rearview mirror.

Spotter Duties

THE SPOTTER'S RESPONSIBILITIES

BE SURE YOU'RE SEEN

Day or night, avoid walking
backward. If you have to, when
walking backwards, be careful
not to trip (check the path).

40 QUESTION FORKLIFT TEST

1. Do you fill out a daily check sheet before each shift prior to using a lift truck?

(YES) (NO)

2. The engine oil should be checked once a week.

(TRUE) (FALSE)

3. Its OK to leave the engine running while refueling.

(TRUE) (FALSE)

4. Only certified and authorized operators are permitted to operate a forklift truck.

(TRUE) (FALSE)

5. O.S.H.A. Standard , the Pedestrian has the right a way with forklifts .

(TRUE) (FALSE)

6. What is a safe distance to maintain when following behind another moving lift truck?

1 , 2 , 3 , (LENGTHS)

7. Always carry loads as close to the ground as possible, or as high as possible.

(CLOSE) (HIGH)

8. It is OK to turn around on a ramp.

(YES) (**NO**)

9. Does a lift truck operator need to sound the horn , when going around blind spots. ?

(YES) (NO)

10. Should you, before changing direction of travel, depress the brake pedal to stop the forklift completely? Then place the directional lever in the forward or reverse direction as desired.

(YES) (NO)

11. Always carry loads with the mast tilted to the forward most position.

(TRUE) (FALSE)

12. When parking a LP powered truck overnight, you should always turn off the service valve. (TRUE) (FALSE)

13. If you are trained to operate a internal combustion engine lift truck, you are allowed to operate any other powered industrial vehicle.

(TRUE) (FALSE)

14. Federal OSHA requires all lift truck operators be certified & authorized

(TRUE) (FALSE)

15. A lift trucks center of gravity always stays in the same place.

(TRUE) (FALSE)

16. Adding a attachment to lift truck does not affect the vehicles lifting capacity.

(TRUE) (FALSE)

17. A truck with a load is less likely to tip over sideways than a truck without a load, if either truck turns too quickly.

(TRUE) (FALSE)

18. It is OK to reach through the mast rails with your hand as long as the truck is not moving.

(TRUE) (FALSE)

19. If a load obstructs your vision, you must travel in reverse or use a spotter to direct you.

(TRUE) (FALSE)

20. Rail Road tracks should be crossed straight ahead not on a angle

(TRUE) (FALSE)

21. Since lift trucks are very heavy vehicles, you do not need to slow down for wet and slippery floors. The weight of the lift truck will provide good traction.

(TRUE) (FALSE)

11. Always carry loads with the mast tilted to the forward most position.

(TRUE) (FALSE)

12. When parking a LP powered truck overnight, you should always turn off the service valve. (TRUE) (FALSE)

13. If you are trained to operate a internal combustion engine lift truck, you are allowed to operate any other powered industrial vehicle.

(TRUE) (FALSE)

14. Federal OSHA requires all lift truck operators be certified & authorized

(TRUE) (FALSE)

15. A lift trucks center of gravity always stays in the same place.

(TRUE) (FALSE)

16. Adding a attachment to lift truck does not affect the vehicles lifting capacity.

(TRUE) (FALSE)

17. A truck with a load is less likely to tip over sideways than a truck without a load, if either truck turns too quickly.

(TRUE) (FALSE)

18. It is OK to reach through the mast rails with your hand as long as the truck is not moving.

(TRUE) (FALSE)

19. If a load obstructs your vision, you must travel in reverse or use a spotter to direct you.

(TRUE) (FALSE)

20. Rail Road tracks should be crossed straight ahead not on a angle

(TRUE) (FALSE)

21. Since lift trucks are very heavy vehicles, you do not need to slow down for wet and slippery floors. The weight of the lift truck will provide good traction.

(TRUE) (FALSE)

22. You should make sure the rear wheels on a semi-trailer are chocked before loading or unloading a trailer.

(TRUE) (FALSE)

23. When picking up a load, forks must be placed under a load as far as possible to the backrest .

(TRUE) (FALSE)

24. If your lift truck does not have an ID or Data Plate you should report it to your supervisor immediately.

(TRUE) (FALSE)

25.It is OK to hang your arm or leg outside the operator's compartment, when carrying a wide load.

(TRUE) (FALSE)

26. Dragging the forks on the ground will cause premature fork wear and compromise the strength of the forks.

(TRUE) (FALSE)

27. With a large load, you can lean outside your truck to get a better view

(TRUE) (FALSE)

28. The lift truck operator should visually inspect dock plates before driving over them.

(TRUE) (FALSE)

29. It is OK to operate a powered industrial vehicle if the horn does not work.

(TRUE) (FALSE)

30. It is OK if you spill a little fuel on the frame of the truck while refueling. The paint on a lift truck is tough.

(TRUE) (FALSE)

31. When a forklift operator removes forks & installs an attachment he / she does not need to have a data plate for that attachment .

(TRUE) (FALSE)

32. It's OK to park a lift truck for a extended period of time with the load elevated, after all it is a lift truck.

(TRUE) (FALSE)

33. When traveling on a flat level surface, you should raise the forks about 10 inches from the floor. With or without a load on them.

(TRUE) (FALSE)

34. Giving someone a ride on your lift truck is OK as long as it is done during working hours and you are careful.

(TRUE) (FALSE)

35. You do not need to refuel gas / diesel forklifts in well ventilated areas .

(TRUE) (FALSE)

36. It is OK to charge lead acid type batteries at lunch time for a quick charge.

(TRUE) (FALSE)

37. After charging your battery always turn off the charger before disconnecting the battery from it.

(TRUE) (FALSE)

38. The safety reverse is used to reverse directions.

(YES) (NO)

39. Should you wear a safety lanyard (tether) when operating a forklift .

(YES) (NO)

40. Do you need to set (parking brake), , lower the forks to the ground , put the machine in neutral . after job is finished , and you are ready to shut down ?

(YES) (NO)

ANSWERS

40 QUESTION FORKLIFT TEST

PLEASE CIRCLE ONE OF THE ANSWERS

1. Do you fill out a daily check sheet before each shift prior to using a lift truck?

(YES) (NO)

2. The engine oil should be checked once a week.

(TRUE) **(FALSE)**

3. Its OK to leave the engine running while refueling.

(TRUE) (FALSE)

4. Only certified and authorized operators are permitted to operate a forklift truck.

(TRUE) (FALSE)

5. O.S.H.A. Standard , the Pedestrian has the right a way with forklifts .

(TRUE) (FALSE)

6.What is a safe distance to maintain when following behind another moving lift truck?

1 , 2 , **3** , (LENGTHS)

7. Always carry loads as close to the ground as possible, or as high as possible.

(CLOSE) (HIGH)

8. It is OK to turn around on a ramp.

(YES) **(NO)**

9. Does a lift truck operator need to sound the horn , when going around blind spots. ?

(YES) (NO)

10. Should you, before changing direction of travel, depress the brake pedal to stop the forklift completely? Then place the directional lever in the forward or reverse direction as desired.

(YES) (NO)

11. Always carry loads with the mast tilted to the forward most position.

(TRUE) **(FALSE)**

12. When parking a LP powered truck overnight, you should always turn off the service valve. (TRUE) (FALSE)

13. If you are trained to operate a internal combustion engine lift truck, you are allowed to operate any other powered industrial vehicle.

(TRUE) **(FALSE)**

14. Federal OSHA requires all lift truck operators be certified & authorized

(TRUE) (FALSE)

15. A lift trucks center of gravity always stays in the same place.

(TRUE) **(FALSE)**

16. Adding a attachment to lift truck does not affect the vehicles lifting capacity.

(TRUE) **(FALSE)**

17. A truck with a load is less likely to tip over sideways than a truck without a load, if either truck turns too quickly.

(TRUE) **(FALSE)**

18. It is OK to reach through the mast rails with your hand as long as the truck is not moving.

(TRUE) **(FALSE)**

19. If a load obstructs your vision, you must travel in reverse or use a spotter to direct you.

(TRUE) (FALSE)

20. Rail Road tracks should be crossed straight ahead not on a angle

(TRUE) **(FALSE)**

21. Since lift trucks are very heavy vehicles, you do not need to slow down for wet and slippery floors. The weight of the lift truck will provide good traction.

(TRUE) **(FALSE)**

22. You should make sure the rear wheels on a semi-trailer are chocked before loading or unloading a trailer.

(TRUE) (FALSE)

23. When picking up a load, forks must be placed under a load as far as possible to the backrest .

(TRUE) (FALSE)

24. If your lift truck does not have an ID or Data Plate you should report it to your supervisor immediately.

(TRUE) (FALSE)

25.It is OK to hang your arm or leg outside the operator's compartment, when carrying a wide load.

(TRUE) **(FALSE)**

26. Dragging the forks on the ground will cause premature fork wear and compromise the strength of the forks.

(TRUE) (FALSE)

27. With a large load, you can lean outside your truck to get a better view

(TRUE) **(FALSE)**

28. The lift truck operator should visually inspect dock plates before driving over them.

(TRUE) (FALSE)

29. It is OK to operate a powered industrial vehicle if the horn does not work.

(TRUE) **(FALSE)**

30. It is OK if you spill a little fuel on the frame of the truck while refueling. The paint on a lift truck is tough.

(TRUE) **(FALSE)**

31. When a forklift operator removes forks & installs an attachment he / she does not need to have a data plate for that attachment .

(TRUE) **(FALSE)**

32. It's OK to park a lift truck for a extended period of time with the load elevated, after all it is a lift truck.

(TRUE) **(FALSE)**

33. When traveling on a flat level surface, you should raise the forks about 10 inches from the floor. With or without a load on them.

(TRUE) **(FALSE)**

34. Giving someone a ride on your lift truck is OK as long as it is done during working hours and you are careful.

(TRUE) **(FALSE)**

35. You do not need to refuel gas / diesel forklifts in well ventilated areas .

(TRUE) **(FALSE)**

36. It is OK to charge lead acid type batteries at lunch time for a quick charge.

(TRUE) **(FALSE)**

37. After charging your battery always turn off the charger before disconnecting the battery from it.

(TRUE) (FALSE)

38. The safety reverse is used to reverse directions.

(YES) (NO)

39. Should you wear a safety lanyard (tether) when operating a forklift .

(YES) (NO)

40. Do you need to set (parking brake), , lower the forks to the ground , put the machine in neutral . after job is finished , and you are ready to shut down ?

(YES) (NO)

Made in United States
Orlando, FL
25 July 2024